Something Happened

AM 3/17

Something Happened

by Cathy Blanford

A book for children
and parents who
have experienced
pregnancy loss.

Illustrated by Phyllis Childers

ISBN: 978-0-9801987-1-3
Library of Congress Control Number: 2007909745

Something Happened
4360 Prospect, Western Springs, IL 60558
www.SomethingHappenedBook.com

Signature Book Printing, Inc.
www.sbpbooks.com
Printed in USA

To those of you whose story this is:
those who have shared it with me already
and those I hope will share it now.

Proceeds from Something Happened will support the work of Still Missed, a perinatal loss support program located in Hinsdale, Illinois. Still Missed, which is a program of the Adventist Midwest Health Systems, has been in existence since 1987. For further information regarding Still Missed or perinatal loss and grief, call 630-856-4497 or e-mail stillmissed@ahss.org.

A Message to Parents

This book addresses a very difficult subject. If you are reading this, it is probably because your family has experienced the death of an expected baby and you are wondering how to help your living children. Some of the pictures and words in this book may feel overwhelming to you. Many years of experience with grieving children have convinced me that this direct approach to the issues is what children, even very young children, need to help them understand and cope with death.

In addition to the pictures and words for children, most pages have a box with words for parents. These words are there to help you understand what your child might be experiencing and why the particular illustrations and text were chosen to help your child deal with this loss. It would be useful to read the book through by yourself before sitting down with your child to read the children's words together.

Cathy Blanford

On the day it happened,

everyone woke up happy.

We were all happy about
the new baby that was coming

to be in our family.

Mommy was happy because she really loved me

and now she was going to have a new baby, too.

It is understandable that Mommy was happy about the new baby. It is also important to communicate clearly that you cherish the child who is already here.

Daddy was happy
because one
kid was great,

Your first child may have never wanted to
share Daddy's time. It is helpful to give
reassurance that nothing will diminish
the relationship that already exists.

and two would be even better!

I was happy because I knew that Mommy and Daddy loved me.

I loved them and my dog, Rusty, but...

It may well be true that your first child has wanted to have a baby brother or sister. At the same time, an older sibling probably has some mixed feelings about the new baby.

I had always wanted a baby sister or brother.

But that night...

It is important to be thoughtful about the way your child learns something bad has happened. You may think your child is not aware that your baby has died or is too young to understand and should not be included in this very sad and important family event. No matter how young they might be, children are very attuned to the feelings of the people they love. If they see Grandma crying or overhear someone's conversation on the phone, they may be scared and worried. Even before anyone knows for sure what to say, your child needs reassurance that someone will be right there taking care of him or her.

something really bad happened.

Instead of going to the hospital to say hello,

The temptation to exclude your child from what is happening at the hospital may be strong. It is important to remember that what your child is imagining is almost always worse than the reality. By bringing your child into the hospital room to visit Mommy and to see the baby and say goodbye, many of the worst fears will be relieved. Your child will be able to see that Mommy is okay and that the baby was too small or too sick to live. Your child will not be left to worry that the baby just disappeared.

...we had to go to
the hospital
to say goodbye.

Mommy and Daddy told me our baby had died,

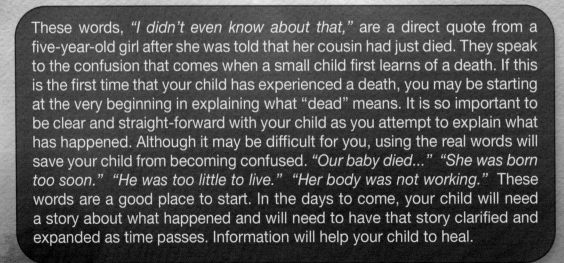

These words, *"I didn't even know about that,"* are a direct quote from a five-year-old girl after she was told that her cousin had just died. They speak to the confusion that comes when a small child first learns of a death. If this is the first time that your child has experienced a death, you may be starting at the very beginning in explaining what "dead" means. It is so important to be clear and straight-forward with your child as you attempt to explain what has happened. Although it may be difficult for you, using the real words will save your child from becoming confused. *"Our baby died..."* *"She was born too soon."* *"He was too little to live."* *"Her body was not working."* These words are a good place to start. In the days to come, your child will need a story about what happened and will need to have that story clarified and expanded as time passes. Information will help your child to heal.

...but I didn't even know about that.

Our baby died...

Maybe you know what happened. Maybe your doctor was able to tell you what caused your baby's death. If so, find the simplest way to give that information to your child. The more information you are able to share in a clear and simple manner, the more your child will be able to understand. Understanding is part of the healing process.

because something happened.

Nobody knows for sure why it happened.
I was scared that it was my fault,

but Mommy and Daddy said
it wasn't anybody's fault.

A young child believes that thoughts can make things happen. If your child even once wished that there would be no new baby, the death of your baby may cause a sense of "I made it happen." Adults can empathize with this feeling, because we often question our own thoughts and actions in the time before the baby came. Was there something we did or failed to do that could have prevented this from happening? We all need information and reassurance about why this tragic thing happened. Your child especially needs to be told again and again that it wasn't anyone's fault. Sometimes bad things just happen.

Sometimes bad things just happen.

I wish I could make our baby come back, but our baby is dead.

The yearning to bring the baby back will be very strong for you and for your child. The difference is that a small child may actually believe that wishing could make it happen. We need to be patient and willing to explain many times the finality of death. This is such a difficult concept for us to accept, and for a child's mind, it is almost impossible. Thus, a child who seems to understand one day, may the next day ask, *"Can we go to the cemetery and get our baby now?"* You might try joining your child in this wish while explaining again why that is not possible. *"I wish we could bring our baby back, but our baby died. Our baby's body totally stopped working. Our baby can't come back."*

Our baby can't come back
no matter how hard we wish.

For a long time, everyone at our house felt sad.

Sometimes I had a tummy ache
and just felt like crying.

You may be surprised that your child does not seem very sad for very long. Instead, you may see your child acting out or demanding more of your attention. Your child may regress and have trouble separating from you or may experience nightmares or illness. Perhaps most bewildering of all, your child may behave as if nothing has happened. All of these behaviors are normal for a child after a death in the family. Regardless of your child's responses, there is a need for information, for an opportunity to express feelings and relate them to what has happened, and for reassurance that love and caring will always be there.

Sometimes I felt really mad
and I didn't even want to play.

And then...

While you may be immersed in grief for a very long time, your child needs something else to happen, validation that life continues. Hopefully, you will have other caring adults who will be able to be with your child when your own energy is very low due to your grieving process. You need to care for yourself in order to be able to care for your child.

something else happened.

We planted a tree and flowers in our backyard for our baby.

Children love ceremony and celebration. Your child needs something concrete which will give permission to remember your baby and to be happy. Planting a tree, creating artwork, or lighting a candle can all be helpful.

Now we have a special place to go and remember.

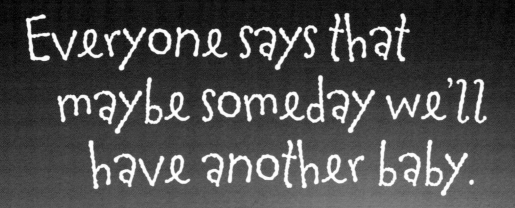

Everyone says that maybe someday we'll have another baby.

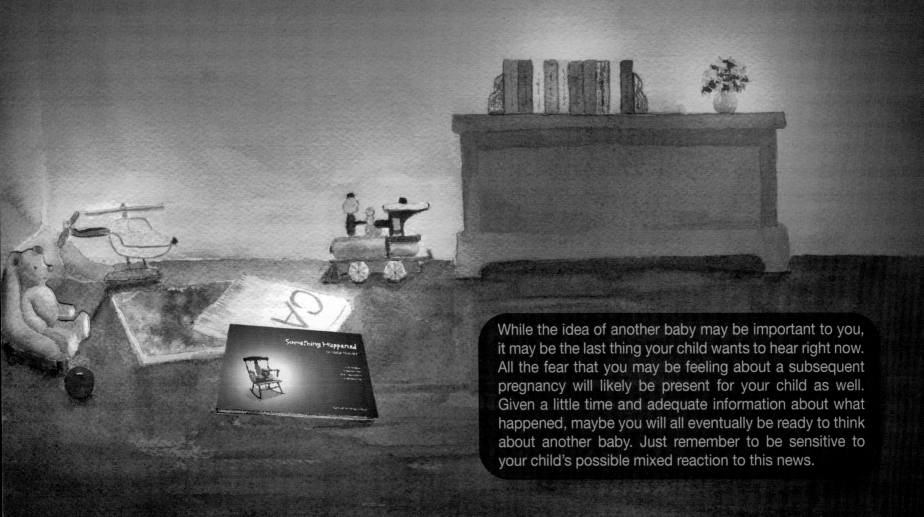

While the idea of another baby may be important to you, it may be the last thing your child wants to hear right now. All the fear that you may be feeling about a subsequent pregnancy will likely be present for your child as well. Given a little time and adequate information about what happened, maybe you will all eventually be ready to think about another baby. Just remember to be sensitive to your child's possible mixed reaction to this news.

Right now, Mommy, Daddy, Rusty and I are still a family.

I love playing with Rusty.
I love playing with
Mommy and Daddy.

Right now this is what is most important. Your child needs to be sure that you are still a family, that you all love each other, and that life can go on and be joyful.

When I wasn't always sure,
Mommy and Daddy helped me know
our love goes on and on.

Author

Cathy Blanford has had over twenty years of experience working with grieving children. She founded and directs Tommy's Kids Support Group at St. Thomas Hospice in Burr Ridge, Illinois. Cathy also serves as a bereavement counselor for Still Missed, a support program for families who have experienced pregnancy loss. She wrote *Something Happened* after seeing the need families have to explain a sudden infant loss to their surviving children. Cathy has a Masters Degree in Early Childhood Development from Erikson Institute in Chicago, Illinois.

Illustrator

Phyllis Childers has worked as an artist, art teacher and art therapist for twenty-five years. She currently works as an artist, illustrator and sculptor in her home studio in Maryland. Phyllis teaches private students, specializing in drawing, watercolor and hand-built ceramics. Phyllis has a Bachelors Degree in Art Education from Indiana University and a Masters Degree in Art Therapy from Lindenwood IV, Lindenwood College, Missouri.

Graphic Designer

Kevin Childers created the design and layout for *Something Happened* and enhanced the illustrations throughout this book using special digital lighting techniques. Kevin is founder of DC Graphics (www.dcgraphics.com) where he works on projects ranging from books and magazines to Web sites and logo design. Kevin is also the Editorial Production Manager for *Kiplinger's Personal Finance* magazine.

The author, illustrator and graphic designer have a long-standing relationship. Phyllis is the mother of Kevin and the Blanford-Childers family relationship dates back to the 1960s. *Something Happened* is their first collaborative effort.